the furry mountain monkeys of Aspen Colorado

by Vince Lahey

Illustrated by Katie Viola

Illustrations executed in watercolor on coldpress paper

Mountain Monkey Publishing
625 Vine St. , Aspen, CO 81611

Printed in South Korea

Library of Congress Cataloging-in-Publication Data
Lahey, Vince.
The Furry Mountain Monkeys of Aspen, Colorado / Written by Vince Lahey / Illustrated by Katie Viola
Summary: Monkeys live in a cave on Aspen Mountain and save the life of a young boy after a ski accident

ISBN 978-1-60402-945-1

1069514

the furry Mountain Monkeys of Aspen Colorado

For Ella

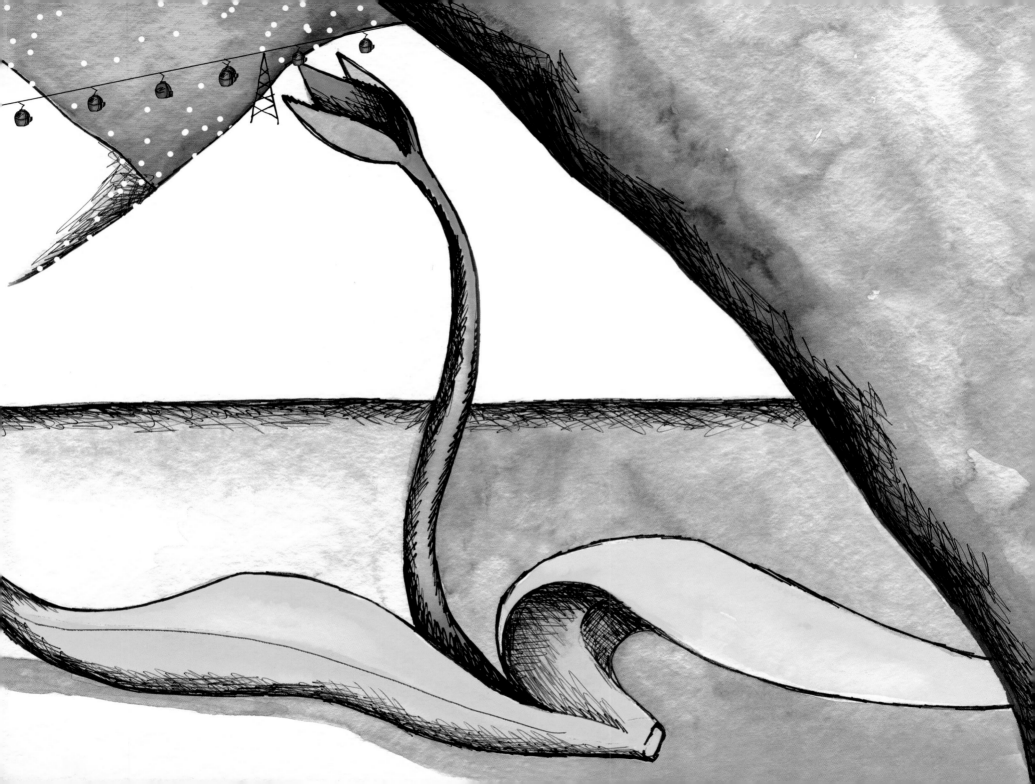

Did you know that monkeys live in Aspen,
and that's the way it has been,
for over a hundred years?

Oh, not to worry, have no fears,
these are really kind monkeys with really small ears.

They're light brown in color and little boy-like in size,
and those who have seen them are thrilled by their eyes.

"They glow in the dark," a miner once said,
as he chugged from a bottle, his own eyes quite red.
"I couldn't believe it, but that's what they were,
monkeys I tell yah, all covered in fur!"

Several have seen them, but never have found,
these quick mountain monkeys asleep on the ground.

They come out at night when the skiers go home,
and that's when these monkeys are quite free to roam.

They slide down
the ski slopes
and swing through
the trees,
until the fur on
their bottoms
is ready to freeze.

Oh, these monkeys
like mountains but
one thing we know,
and that is a
monkey can't
live in the snow.

Monkeys like jungles
as hot as July,
with trees so dense
they block out the sky.

So how could it be
that monkeys exist,
in a place where blizzards
for weeks can persist?

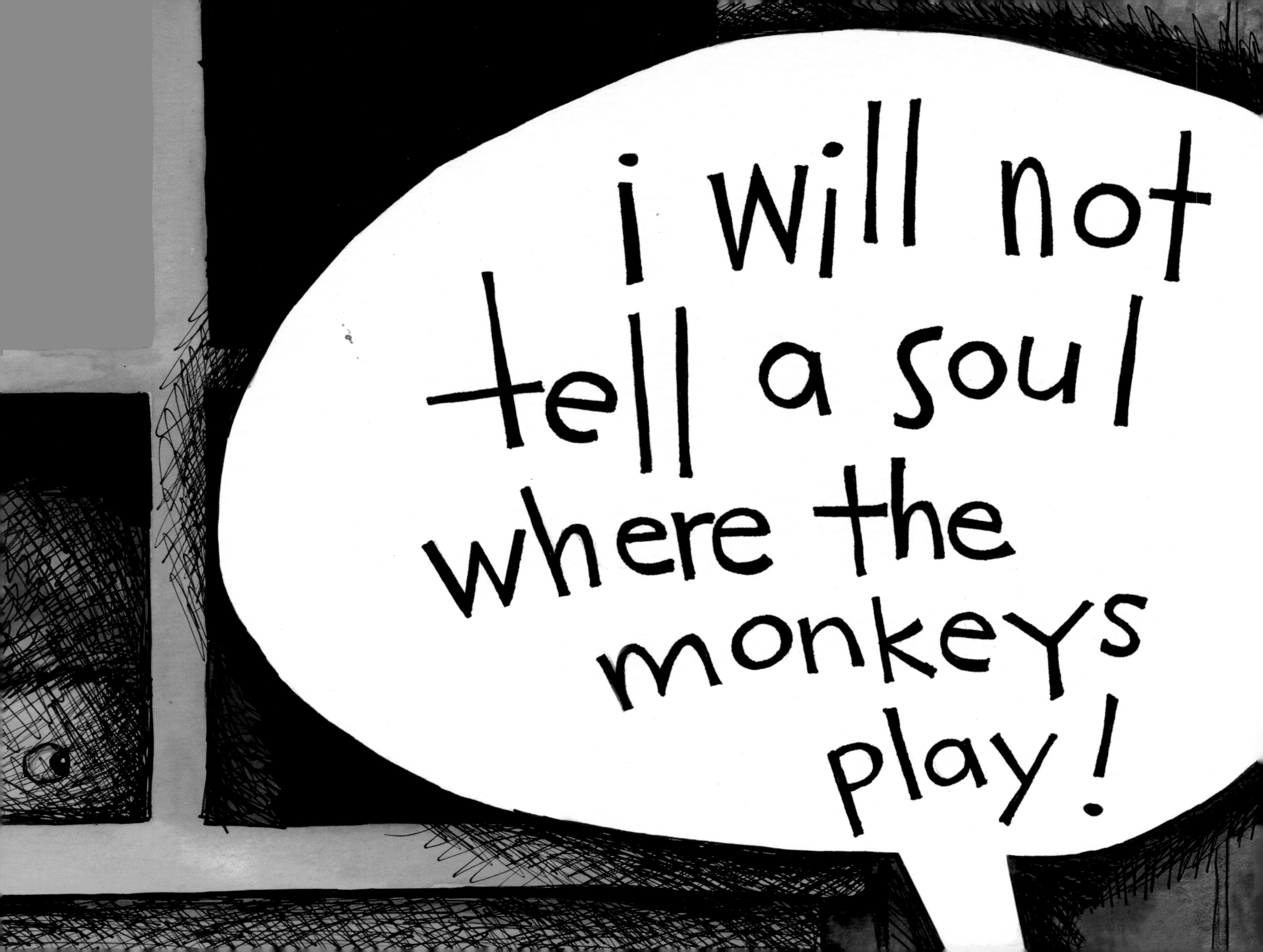
i will not tell a soul where the monkeys play!

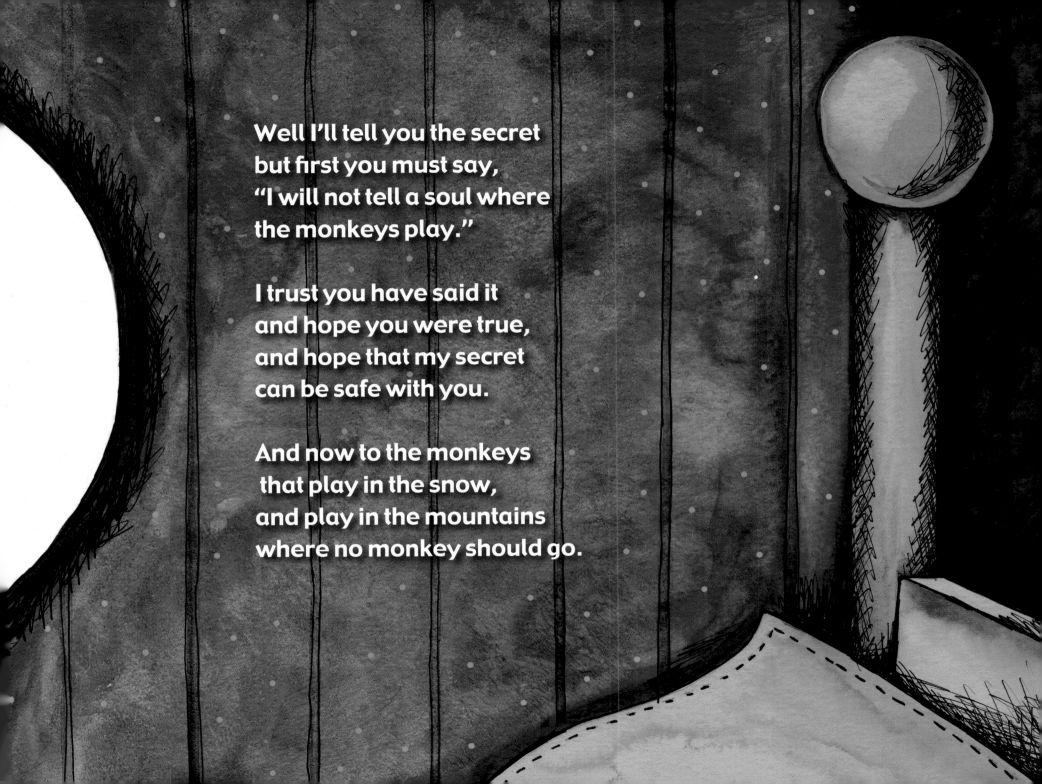

Well I'll tell you the secret
but first you must say,
"I will not tell a soul where
the monkeys play."

I trust you have said it
and hope you were true,
and hope that my secret
can be safe with you.

And now to the monkeys
that play in the snow,
and play in the mountains
where no monkey should go.

If you ski up on Aspen
you know of the humps,
that the skiers refer to
as simply the dumps.

The dumps are what's left
from years of hard mining,
and deep in one cave
a light is still shining.

Now it will come to you as no great surprise,
that this is the light of furry mountain monkey eyes.

Deep in one cave the monkeys have found,
a hot sulfur spring that springs from the ground.

Stranger than that and a sight to be seen,
are all of the plants that are growing so green.

Remember these monkeys have glowing green eyes,
and with this light they create the skies.

They give the plants energy just like the sun,
and help the plants grow as if they were one.

The cave is their secret
and I'll never say,
the exact location where
the monkeys play.

You see I owe them my life
for one day while skiing,
I ran into a tree and
almost stopped being.

Lucky for me
the monkeys were there,
and risked their own secret
to give me their care.

They took me into their cave
and gave me attention,
and I stood in their world
with a mild apprehension.

I swam in their hot springs
and began to grow strong,
and the love of the monkeys
made me want to stay long.

But as the days grew to weeks
I knew it was time,
to leave this kind family
and return to mine.

The monkeys were sad
on the day that I left,
and I was so sad that
I openly wept.

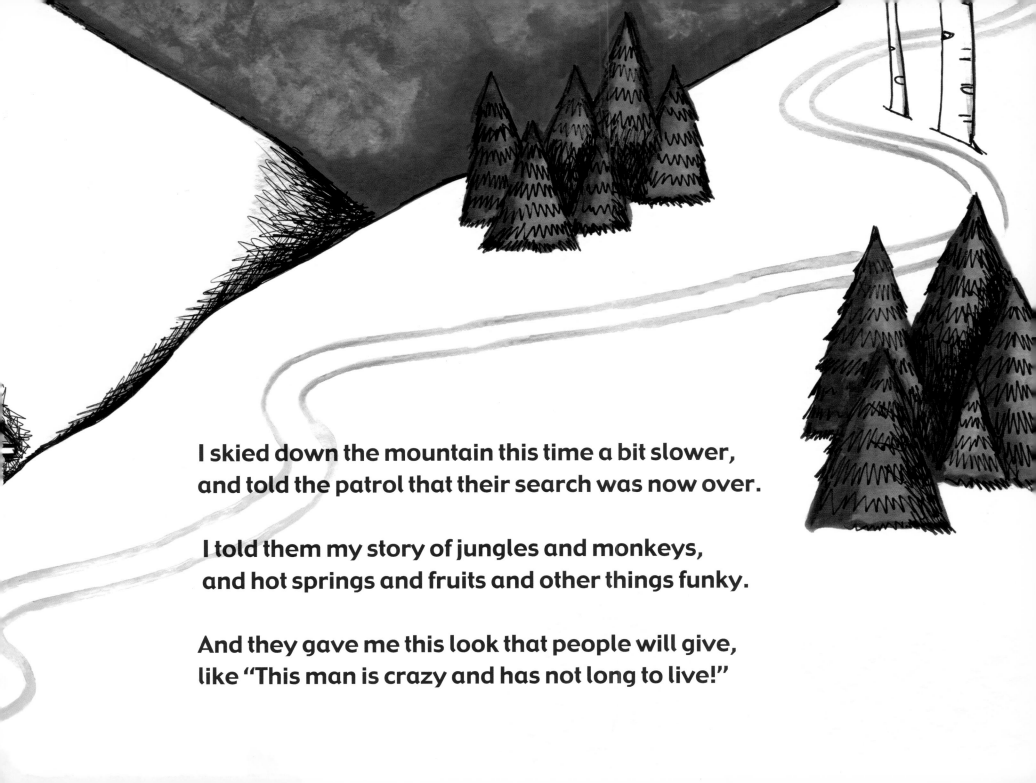

I skied down the mountain this time a bit slower,
and told the patrol that their search was now over.

I told them my story of jungles and monkeys,
and hot springs and fruits and other things funky.

And they gave me this look that people will give,
like "This man is crazy and has not long to live!"

But I tell you my friend that this is the truth,
and all of this happened when I was a youth.

Now I am older and late in the night,
I'll look to the mountain in search of their light.

And sometimes I'll see just a small dot of green,
as they swing through the trees igniting the scene.

And some say I'm crazy but I say to you,
look to the mountain and you'll see them too!